**q**uestion

**q**uilt

**q**ueen

"Quack, quack, quack."

"Quickly, **q**uickly!" said Mom.

"Quietly, **q**uietly!"
said Mom.

"Quickly, **q**uickly!"
said Mother Duck.

"Quickly, **q**uickly!
Look out for the cars!"

"Quack, quack, quack."

Quick, **q**uick, **q**uick!
Give me a lick!
*Lick, lick, lick.*
You have to be **q**uick!